AWAY FROM HOME

JOANNE CLAIRMONT

www.teensawayfromhome.com

Away from Home
Joanne Clairmont

Paperback Edition First Published in the United Kingdom
in 2017 by aSys Publishing

eBook Edition First Published in the United Kingdom
in 2017 by aSys Publishing

Disclaimer
This is a work of fiction. All characters and incidents are products
of the author's imagination and any resemblance to actual people
or events is coincidental or fictionalised.

ISBN: 978-1-910757-89-5

aSys Publishing
http://www.asys-publishing.co.uk

AWAY FROM HOME

Contents

The Runaway Teenager

The Unaccompanied Minor

The Unsettled Teenager

The Settled Teenager

The Challenging Teenager

Independent Teenager

The Runaway Teenager

Please don't run

Please don't run, I wait, I fear, I care for you.
I know how you might be feeling, I am new, you are unsure, so you fear. You are confused and want a place of familiarity.

I wait patiently, the night time comes, I don't see you. I make phone calls to friends. My mind running, my mind checking, I start worrying.

999 calls to police I make – what were they wearing, describe the person to me. Have they gone missing before?

I wait in hope. I look at my mobile, my mind with worry past midnight now. No sleeping for me, my mind wondering, my mind pondering.

A knock on the door I hear, no smile on her face she bears. Where have you been? Are you fine? Are you hungry? Or angry?

Do you want to talk?

Silence is the order of the day

Please don'tt run – I care for you.

This is the life I know

I run because that's all I know. Don't look for me, don't call the police on me, I run because that's all I know.   -

You don't understand me, so don't try to fix me, I run because that's all I know.

Don't try to find me, just leave me, I will find my way home.

Emergency Placement (teenager)

I have a nice home for the night. I do not think I will be here in the morning. I am not used to a base or a familiar face, I don't think I will be here in the morning.

I will sleep here for the night and make up my mind in the morning.

The Unaccompanied Minor

From the East to the West

From the East to the West, how I got here is none of your business, no more questions, I am tired. I need to rest you don't know how I feel, no family just alone.

I am told by the Social Worker that I am going to a new home, they will look after me. I fear I despair, will I fit in? Fear is my friend.

Feeling alone I enter into the unknown, happy families they play, my state of mind not intact, questions they ask, more questions, questions have become my friend.

This is your room, what do you eat? These are the rules and don't forget.

Have you any questions for me? At last, it is my turn, I am too tired, not for now.

Meetings and greetings, happy families I see, where is mine I am longing to see. Don't do this and don't do that, we do it this way here.

Feeling a sense of loss, I stay in my room, a place of no distraction, a place to think, a place to recall the events.

Don't judge me until you have been through what I have. Questions, questions are the order of the day.

The Wheels on my suitcase go round and round

The suitcase is my friend. Travelling to and fro, not knowing where the suitcase will end up. I pack it, I unpack it, I pull it and I drag it.

The wheels on my suitcase go round and round never really having a final destination.

At last, I rest it in a comfortable home. I will leave it open just in case the wheels need to go around again.

From village life to London life

From village life to London life, where ever the wind takes me.
From rural areas to built-up areas, wherever there is a foster carer.

Do I have to move again? My heart can't take the beats. The beats of
fear, the beats of worry the beats of not knowing where I am going
in a hurry.

From village life to London life, I will have to adjust my way of living.

The Unsettled Teenager

I landed at your door

I wake up to strange voices, strange house, strange bedroom. How did I land at your door?

Give me a break, stop checking me, stop asking me if I am ok.

How did I land at your door?

Rules are new to me never had rules before. Sorry, can't keep rules.

Stop caring, stop staring, stop checking.

How did I land at your door?

Expect me to play happy families, no chance, I will be flying like a dove.

How did I land at your door?

Give me a break and let me be, stop checking, stop asking, stop feeling.

How did I land at your door?

From place to place I ponder

From place to place I wonder, feeling tired and weary, will you be my mum and dad?

This is your home now, very nice people.

From place to place I wonder, from place to place I ponder.

Pack your bags you're leaving for the next adventure.

From place to place I wonder.

Don't know if I am coming or going

I don't know if I am coming or going, what I do know I am not staying.

Don't try to control me, don't try to make things better.

I don't know if I am coming or going, what I do know I am not staying.

I don't want your life, your rules or your kindness.

I am not an experiment, I am a person who has a mum and dad, don't try to control me to fit into your family.

Let things be.

I don't want your life, your rules or your kindness.

Thank you.

I am not feeling it here

I am not feeling it here, I am confused and full of despair,

I am not feeling it here, nice you may be but I am not feeling it here.

To and fro I am blown in the wind, I am just not feeling it here.

Let me say goodbye and return to a place of security.

Trauma

I am not sure what it looks like but I sure know how it feels like. One day I am up and the next day I am down. Don't blame me if I walk with a frown.

You tell me it would pass with time, but the feelings are confusing and my world is reducing. Reducing to tears, fears and not knowing.

My world will get brighter if I focus my mind on brighter and better things.

I am living with strangers

I am living with people I do not know.

How do you expect me to feel? How do you expect me to behave? I am living with people I do not know.

You smile, I smile, you talk, I nod. How do you expect me to behave? I am living with people I do not know.

Forgive me if I stay in my room and block out the pain and the blame. I am living with people I do not know.

Only time will tell if this would change. I am living with people I do not know.

Your culture is different your food is different. I am living with people I do not know.

Time will be my healer.

The Settled Teenager

A person once more

When I first met you, I did not know if I could trust you.
You were warm and caring and showed me life was not so frightening.

You gave me hope and strength to go on by being there when I needed.

Settled, I feel a person once more.

I will settle here

This home is nice, I will settle here hopefully I will not move again in a hurry. What are the rules? I will see if I can handle, maybe from a different angle.

Can I bring a friend? Can they sleep over? Can I bring my memories to cope with the changes?

Stuck in a place of safety

I am stuck in a place of safety. Morning and night I do not leave my room.

You wonder if I am depressed, you wonder if I am alright but I prefer to stay in my room to gather my thoughts.

My thoughts and dreams are in my room, do not disturb I need to think.

My place of comfort and safety lie here, so don't just walk into my place of peace.

Hopes and dreams

In you I trust for my hopes and dreams, I feel abandoned, lost like a ship at sea.

In you, I trust for my hopes and dreams.

Don't give up on me because I am challenging, I need you to be there for me.

In you I trust for my hopes and dreams.

I try to block out my past and think of the future.

In you I trust for my hopes and dreams.

Dreams of becoming a Doctor, dreams of having a future.

Do you really care for me?

In you I trust for my hopes and dreams.

Time is passing - I am feeling secure hope I will be able to stay until independence.

In you I trust for my hopes and dreams.

The Challenging Teenager

Don't tell me what to do

Don't tell me what do you - you are not my mother. I eat and leave dishes, I swear, I lie I do not do my chores, but you still care for me.

I shout I play loud music, you remind of the rules all because you care for me.

I come in late, I use the bus excuse, you remind me of the rules all because you care for me.

You make sure you have my interest at heart. You make sure I am safe, while I do not stick to the rules.

I start feeling secure, I open up slowly but surely, I can cope with some of the rules now.

I don't mind you telling me what to do because you care for me.

It is not cool

It is not cool to lie, steal and smoke weed but it comes with the job, you say.

Don't try to change me, accept me, I will turn around. Give me space, give me time, I will change.

Don't judge me you don't know my past.

Like a bird without wings, I have landed at your door.

No school today

No school today I am not going, I stress, I do not like tests I am not going.

No school today my stomach is hurting. Your teacher has told me that you have not been going.

Don't wake me up, I will be sleeping, no school today no stress I feel.

Do me a favour

Do me a favour stop asking me about my past, where I have been, stop probing and stop comparing.

I tell my story at every greeting and not really bothered about the meeting.

My story is the same old. It does not change with the household.

Thanks for being understanding.

Don't come into my room

Don't come into my room I don't like it. My life, my story, my past and future are in my private space.

Don't come into my room I don't like it, what you see is what you get! My bedroom is not always a reflection of how I am feeling.

Spot checks, professional checks, clean checks and unannounced checks. Don't come into my room I don't like it.

You go creeping

You think I am sleeping so 2 am in the morning you go creeping to eating what your heart desires.

This is not part of the house rules but your desire is on fire, your mind and thoughts are going down a one-way street.

Everything is for your own pleasure.

Your night time is my day time

Don't wake me up it is only 2 pm in the afternoon. Your night time is my day time.

You tell me not to shower and wash my clothes way past the midnight hour. You tell me not to play my music late and this is not up for debate.

Your night time is my day time.

I am sick

I am sick, I need to be fixed immediately, take me to Accident and Emergency. Why do I wait, can't they see I need attention almost immediately.

Why am I waiting I should be seen first, no time to wait in case I get worse.

Hurry them up, I need to be seen my patience is running very thin.

I can't wait I have to leave no time to wait around to be seen.

Food

Food is my great comforter. It comforts my heart and the missing puzzle that I can't put together. Food is my great comforter.

Food is my great comforter. It comforts the hole in my heart, my desire not to start. Food is my great comforter.

Food is my great comforter when I am down when I am not sound. When questions can't be answered food is my great comforter.

You see it is not greed you have me all wrong. Food is my great comforter I find the person within.

Don't turn of the lights

Don't turn off the lights. I can see the shadows of the past, the shadows of the future, don't turn off the lights.

I came to you in the light, but the darkness holds me back, don't turn off the lights at night.

Bring me to the light where I had a family life. Don't turn off the lights at night.

Appointments

Appointments, appointments I endure from Doctors, Nurses to Review meeting I ignore.

Leave me alone, I am not going too many appointments my head is spinning.

You say it is for my own good, health and education I understood. Appointments, appointments I endure, leave it to me, and I surely ignore.

Minicab service please

Could you come and collect me, it's getting too dark, can't walk the streets alone in the dark.

Could you come and collect me I have missed the last bus and also forgotten my oyster card.

Could you come and collect me, leave what you are doing and come.

Returning home

With every passing moment, I am filled with hope, I will return to my home I pray.

Days, weeks and months go past, I will return to my home at last.

Meetings and meetings I go, like a lost sheep I run to and fro, I will return to the home I know.

The years go past and the memories fade, I will return to my home one day.

Independent Teenager

You gave me hope

You gave me life you gave me stability look at me now I turned into somebody.

From the far West I came, you took me in as your own.

You gave me hope and a secure feeling. I could not appreciate it in the way I was dealing.

I have now grown ready to depart I will always hold you dear to my heart.

Memories

Every passing moment I was with you will be a memory for the future.

Every photo taken will be captured in my mind.

You talking, you laughing are captured memories for the future.

Wonderful you have come back to see me

Wonderful you have come back to see me, looking well, looking confident you have made your own way through life, not letting opportunities pass you by.

You took my advice. You knew I meant well, you did your best to secure your future.

You worked hard. You kept your head down.

You were not perfect, but you cared for your future.

Wonderful you have come back to see me. I was not a shadow in your mind I was a reality you did not leave behind. You felt safe and secure.

Wonderful you have come back to see me.

A distant person you are not, my heart holds you dearly, a brighter future in store.

Wonderful you have come back to see me.

QUESTIONS FOR READERS

Question 1	How did you feel about your bedroom when you were a child and how do you feel about your bedroom now? Did you have to share your bedroom, if so how did you feel about sharing? Why do you think a bedroom is an important space to a young person in a foster home?
Question 2	Have you ever used food for comfort when you were feeling low or missing someone? Did it make you feel better? Do you think some young people may use food as a form of comfort if they are feeling low or worried about something?
Question 3	Why do you think some young people run away from home?
Question 4	Have you ever travelled abroad to another country? How would you feel if you are expected to start a new life away from your family and friends?

Question 5	Have you either left home or a place that you were attached to – to go to university or move into your own home. How did it make you feel at the time? How do you think a fostered young person may feel leaving a Home that they may be attached to?
Question 6	If you are an adult reading this book would you consider fostering teenagers? A secure base or a place of safety can help a young person reach their full potential. Do you agree or disagree with this statement?
Question 7	The last page of this book shows that if you give a young person in care your time, patience and are caring towards them, they can achieve with time. What is your opinion on this?

Finally, the reality is that fostering teenagers can be challenging, but the rewards outweigh the challenges.